Success
Assessment Papers

Non-Verbal
Reasoning

age 6 – 7

Lisa Murrell

Sample page

paper number for
quick reference

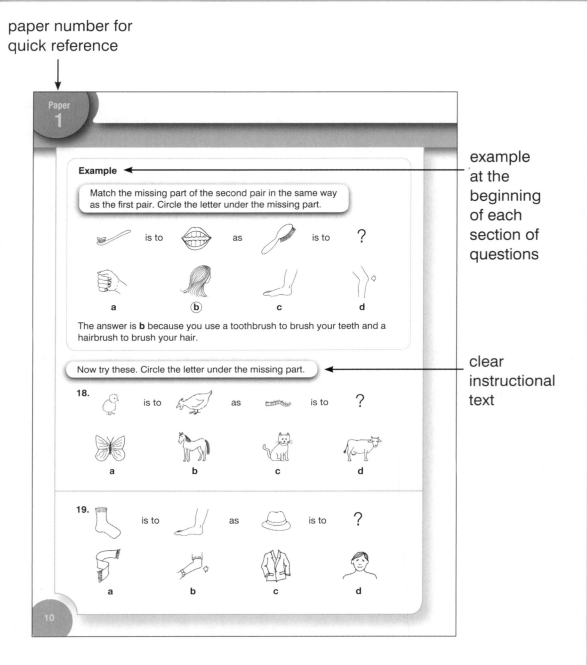

Example

Match the missing part of the second pair in the same way
as the first pair. Circle the letter under the missing part.

is to   as   is to   **?**

a   (b)   c   d

The answer is **b** because you use a toothbrush to brush your teeth and a
hairbrush to brush your hair.

Now try these. Circle the letter under the missing part.

18.   is to   as   is to   **?**

a   b   c   d

19.   is to   as   is to   **?**

a   b   c   d

10

example
at the
beginning
of each
section of
questions

clear
instructional
text

Contents

PAPER 1

Example

> Which is the odd one out? Circle the letter underneath it.

a   b   c   ⓓ

The answer is **d** because the shark is the only animal that lives in the sea.

> Now try these. Which is the odd one out? Circle the letter underneath it.

1.

a   b   c   d

2.

a   b   c   d

3.

a   b   c   d

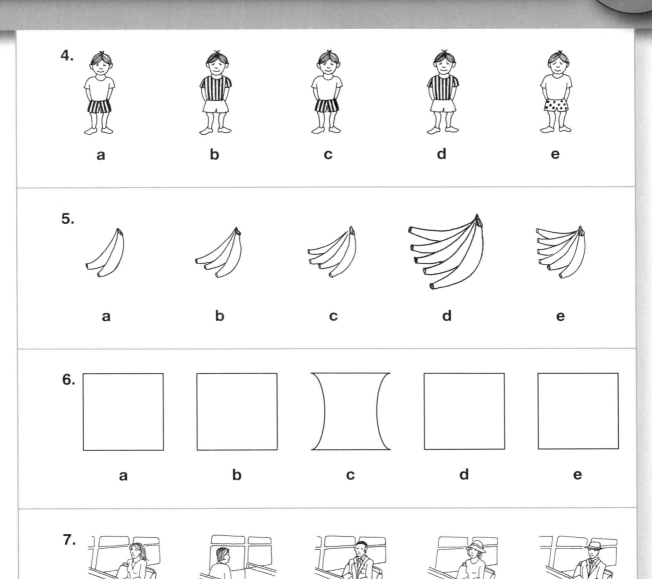

4.

   a   b   c   d   e

5.

   a   b   c   d   e

6.

   a   b   c   d   e

7.

   a   b   c   d   e

/7

Example

Which one comes next? Circle the letter underneath it.

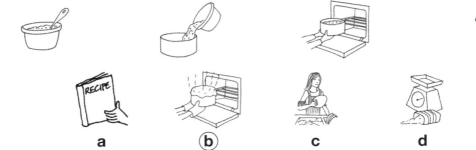

The answer is **b** because it is the next thing that happens in the "story". When you have baked a cake you take it out of the oven.

Now try these. Which one comes next? Circle the letter underneath it.

8.

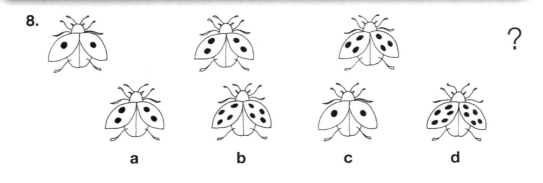

9.

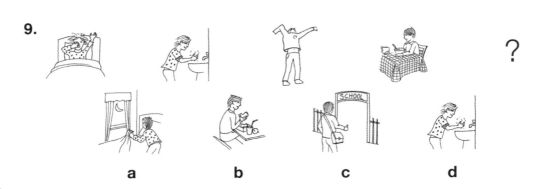

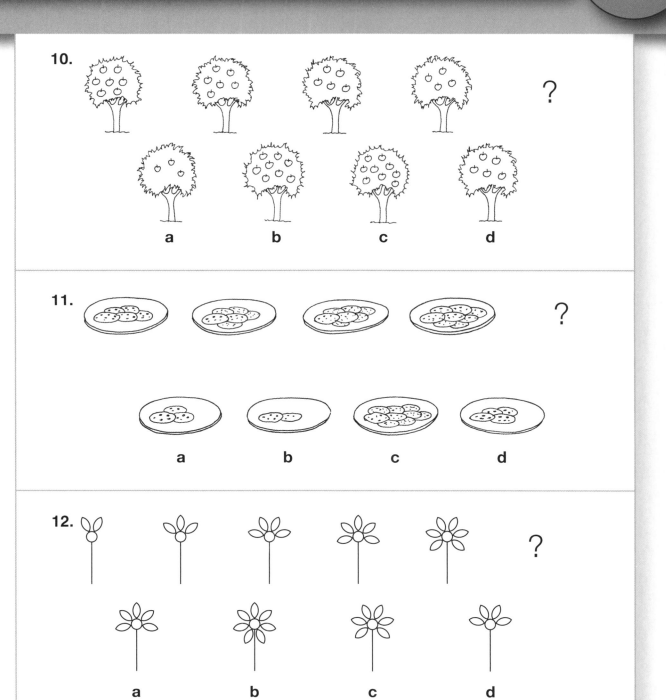

10.

                              ?

     a   b   c   d

11.

                                ?

     a   b   c   d

12.

                                ?

     a   b   c   d

/5

Example

Complete the grid by finding the missing square.
Circle the letter under the square.

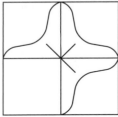

a   **b**   **c**   **(d)**

The answer is **d** because it completes the shape and also finishes the cross in the middle.

Now try these. Circle the letter under the missing square.

13.

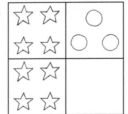

a   **b**   **c**   **d**

14.

a   **b**   **c**   **d**

15.

a   b   c   d

16.

a   b   c   d

17.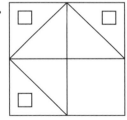

a   b   c   d

/5

Example

Match the missing part of the second pair in the same way as the first pair. Circle the letter under the missing part.

 is to as is to **?**

a **(b)** **c** **d**

The answer is **b** because you use a toothbrush to brush your teeth and a hairbrush to brush your hair.

Now try these. Circle the letter under the missing part.

18. is to as is to **?**

a **b** **c** **d**

19. is to as is to **?**

a **b** **c** **d**

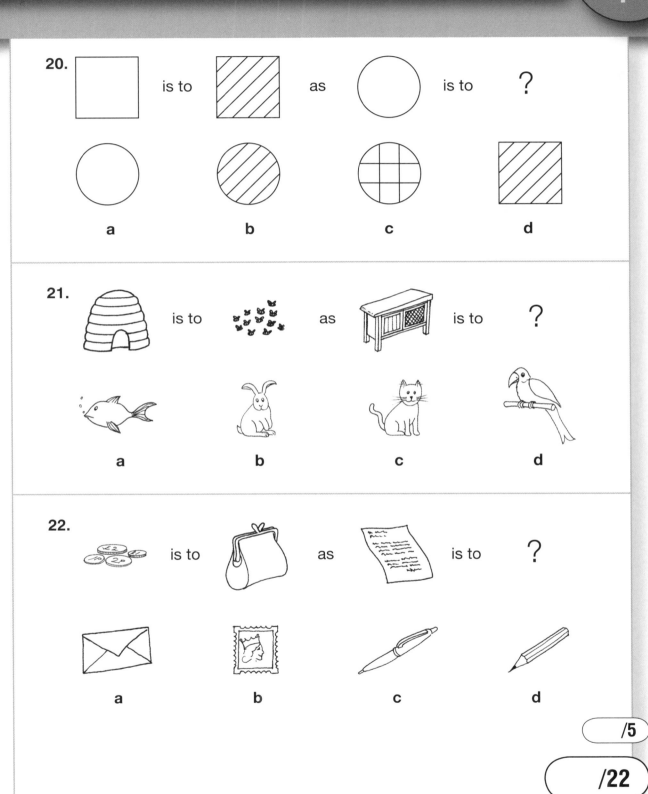

20.

is to　　　　　　　as　　　　　　　is to　　　?

a　　　　　　　　b　　　　　　　　c　　　　　　　　d

21.

is to　　　　　　　as　　　　　　　is to　　　?

a　　　　　　　　b　　　　　　　　c　　　　　　　　d

22.

is to　　　　　　　as　　　　　　　is to　　　?

a　　　　　　　　b　　　　　　　　c　　　　　　　　d

/5

/22

PAPER 2

Example

> Which is the odd one out? Circle the letter underneath it.

a   **b**   **c**   (**d**)

The answer is **d** because the shark is the only animal that lives in the sea.

> Now try these. Which is the odd one out? Circle the letter underneath it.

1.

a   **b**   **c**   **d**

2.

a   **b**   **c**   **d**

3.

a   **b**   **c**   **d**

4.

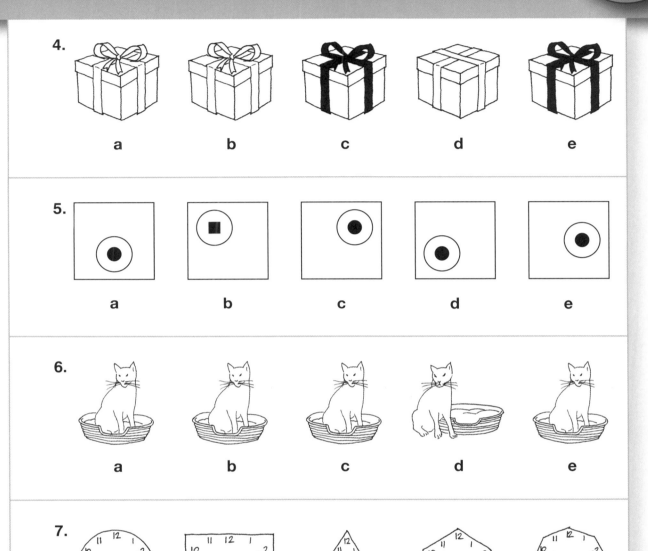

a   b   c   d   e

5.

a   b   c   d   e

6.

a   b   c   d   e

7.

a   b   c   d   e

Example

Which one comes next? Circle the letter underneath it.

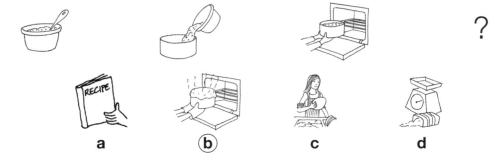

The answer is **b** because it is the next thing that happens in the "story". When you have baked a cake you take it out of the oven.

Now try these. Which one comes next? Circle the letter underneath it.

8.

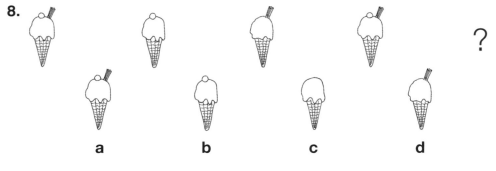

9.

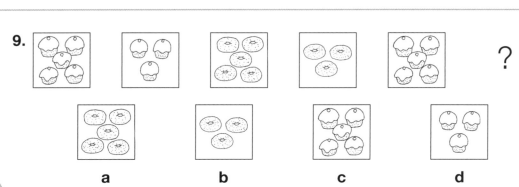

10.

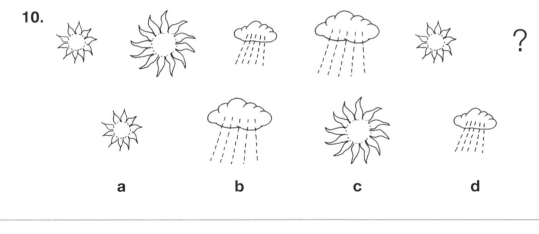

   a   b   c   d

11.

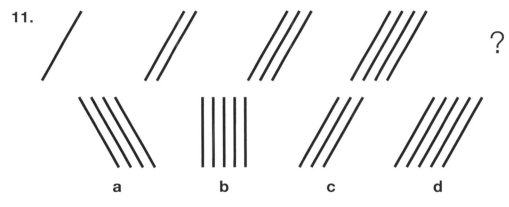

   a   b   c   d

12.

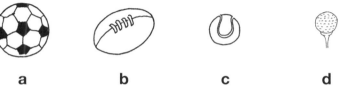

   a   b   c   d

/5

Example

Complete the grid by finding the missing square.
Circle the letter under the square.

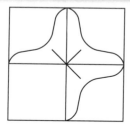

a   b   c   (d)

The answer is **d** because it completes the shape and also finishes the cross in the middle.

Now try these. Circle the letter under the missing square.

13.

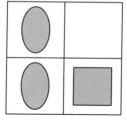

a   b   c   d

14.

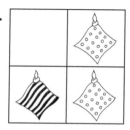

a   b   c   d

15.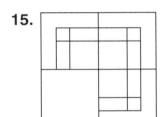

                                   a   b   c   d

16.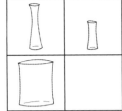

                                   a   b   c   d

17.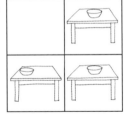

                                   a   b   c   d

/5

Example

Match the missing part of the second pair in the same way as the first pair. Circle the letter under the missing part.

 is to as is to ?

a **b** **c** **d**

The answer is **b** because you use a toothbrush to brush your teeth and a hairbrush to brush your hair.

Now try these. Circle the letter under the missing part.

18.

 is to as is to ?

a **b** **c** **d**

19.

 is to as is to ?

a **b** **c** **d**

20.

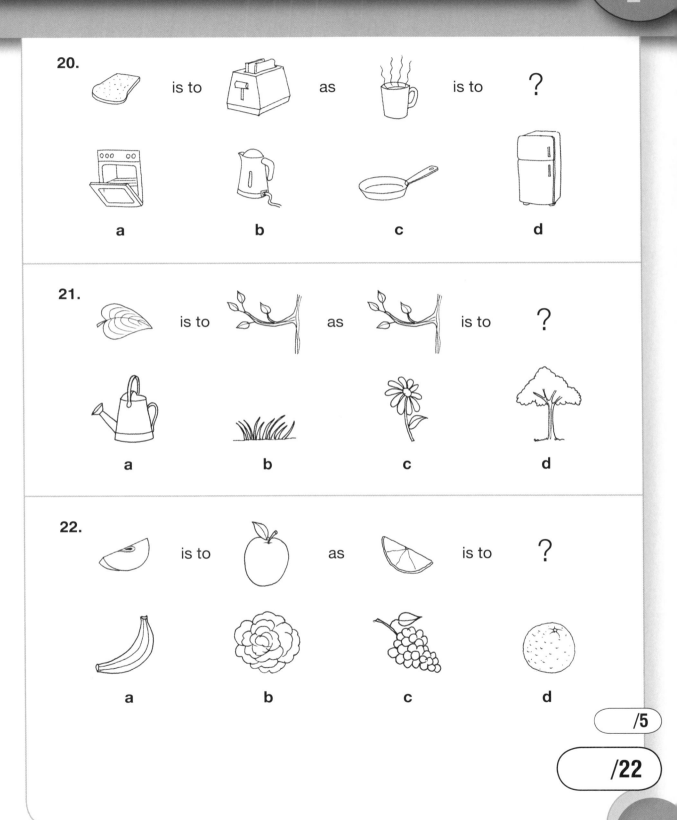

is to ... as ... is to ?

a   b   c   d

21.

is to ... as ... is to ?

a   b   c   d

22.

is to ... as ... is to ?

a   b   c   d

/5

/22

PAPER 3

Example

Which is the odd one out? Circle the letter underneath it.

a b c d

The answer is **d** because the shark is the only animal that lives in the sea.

Now try these. Which is the odd one out? Circle the letter underneath it.

1.

a b c d

2.

a b c d

3.

 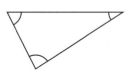

a b c d

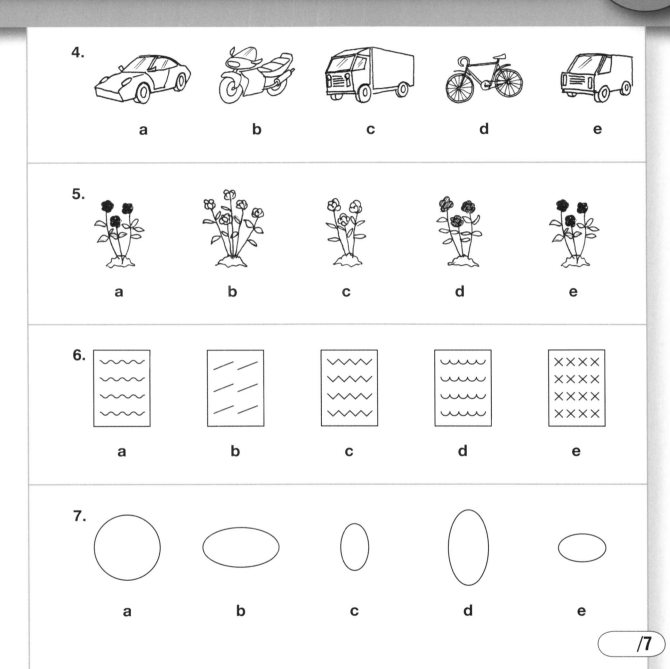

4.

   a   b   c   d   e

5.

   a   b   c   d   e

6.

   a   b   c   d   e

7.

   a   b   c   d   e

/7

Example

Which one comes next? Circle the letter underneath it.

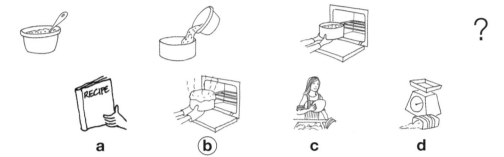

The answer is **b** because it is the next thing that happens in the "story". When you have baked a cake you take it out of the oven.

Now try these. Which one comes next? Circle the letter underneath it.

8.

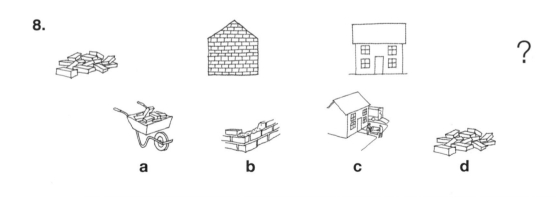

9.

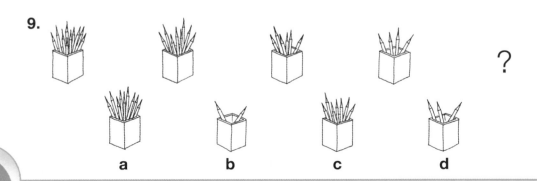

10.

11.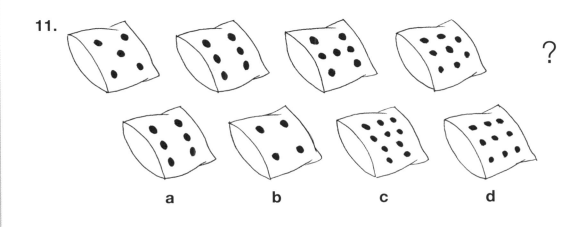

12.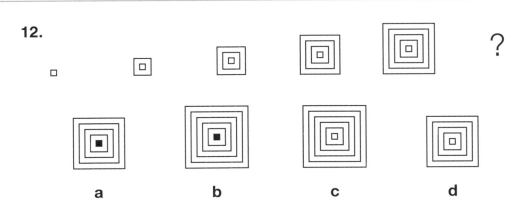

/5

Example

Complete the grid by finding the missing square.
Circle the letter under the square.

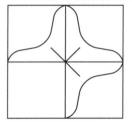

a

b

c

d

The answer is **d** because it completes the shape and also finishes the cross in the middle.

Now try these. Circle the letter under the missing square.

13.

a

b

c

d

14.

a

b

c

d

15.

            c

     a   b   c   d

16.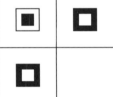

     a   b   c   d

17.

     a   b   c   d

/5

Example

Match the missing part of the second pair in the same way as the first pair. Circle the letter under the missing part.

 is to as is to ?

a　　　　**b**　　　　**c**　　　　**d**

The answer is **b** because you use a toothbrush to brush your teeth and a hairbrush to brush your hair.

Now try these. Circle the letter under the missing part.

18.
 is to as is to ?

a　　　　**b**　　　　**c**　　　　**d**

19.
 is to as is to ?

a　　　　**b**　　　　**c**　　　　**d**

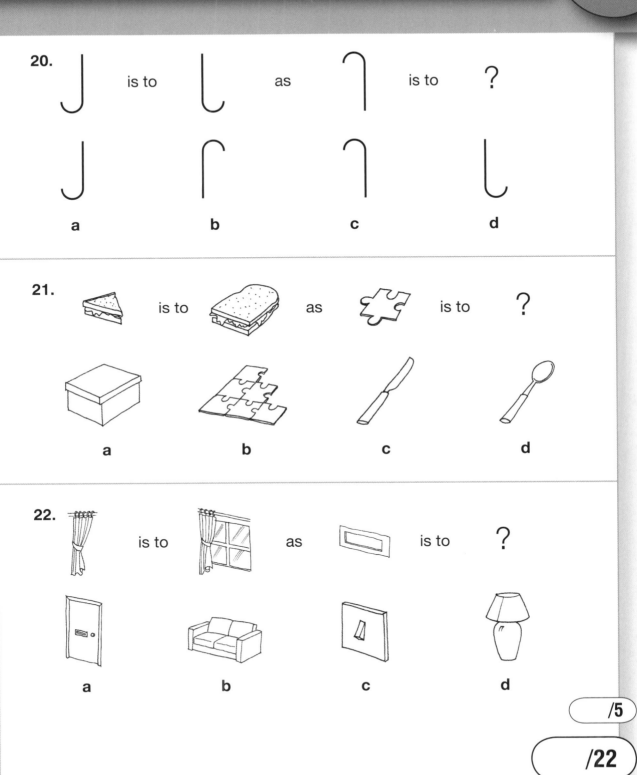

20. 〜 is to 〜 as 〜 is to ?

a   b   c   d

21. is to as is to ?

a   b   c   d

22. is to as is to ?

a   b   c   d

/5

/22

PAPER 4

Example

> Which is the odd one out? Circle the letter underneath it.

a   b   c   **d**

The answer is **d** because the shark is the only animal that lives in the sea.

> Now try these. Which is the odd one out? Circle the letter underneath it.

1.

a   b   c   d

2.

a   b   c   d

3.

a   b   c   d

4.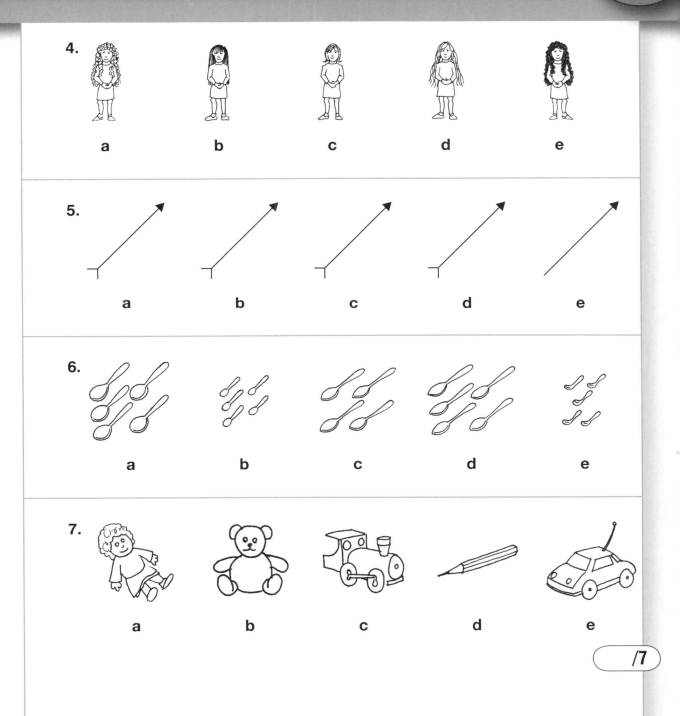

a   b   c   d   e

5.

a   b   c   d   e

6.

a   b   c   d   e

7.

a   b   c   d   e

/7

Example

Which one comes next? Circle the letter underneath it.

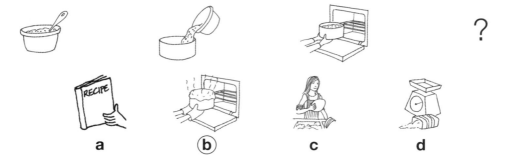

The answer is **b** because it is the next thing that happens in the "story". When you have baked a cake you take it out of the oven.

Now try these. Which one comes next? Circle the letter underneath it.

8.

9.

10.

1 2	4 5	7 8	10 11	13 14
3	6	9	12	15

?

18 19	15 16	16 17	12 13
20	17	18	14
a	b	c	d

11.

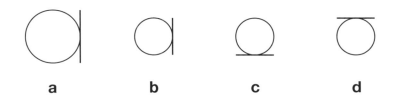

    a   b   c   d

12.

a   b   c   d

/5

Example

Complete the grid by finding the missing square.
Circle the letter under the square.

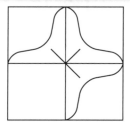

a   b   c   (d)

The answer is **d** because it completes the shape and also finishes the cross in the middle.

Now try these. Circle the letter under the missing square.

13.

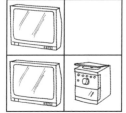

a   b   c   d

14.

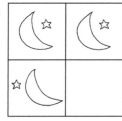

a   b   c   d

15.

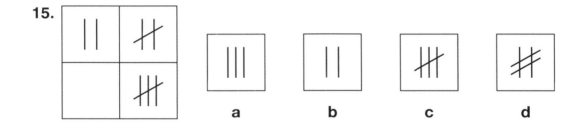

a   b   c   d

16.

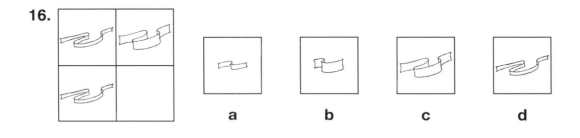

a   b   c   d

17.

a   b   c   d

/5

Example

Match the missing part of the second pair in the same way as the first pair. Circle the letter under the missing part.

 is to as is to

   a   **ⓑ**   c   d

The answer is **b** because you use a toothbrush to brush your teeth and a hairbrush to brush your hair.

Now try these. Circle the letter under the missing part.

18. is to as is to **?**

   a   b   c   d

19. is to as is to **?**

   a   b   c   d

Success
Assessment Papers

Non-Verbal Reasoning

age 6 – 7

Answer booklet

Answer booklet: Success Assessment papers Non-Verbal Reasoning 6–7 years

PAPER 1
 1. c
 2. b
 3. d
 4. e
 5. d
 6. c
 7. b
 8. b
 9. c
10. a
11. c
12. b
13. b
14. b
15. a
16. d
17. a
18. a
19. d
20. b
21. b
22. a

PAPER 2
 1. c
 2. d
 3. a
 4. d
 5. b
 6. d
 7. a
 8. b

 9. d
10. c
11. d
12. a
13. b
14. d
15. d
16. b
17. a
18. a
19. c
20. b
21. d
22. d

PAPER 3
 1. a
 2. c
 3. a
 4. d
 5. b
 6. b
 7. a
 8. c
 9. b
10. c
11. d
12. c
13. b
14. a
15. c
16. b
17. c

18. c
19. b
20. b
21. b
22. a

PAPER 4
 1. d
 2. a
 3. c
 4. c
 5. e
 6. c
 7. d
 8. c
 9. c
10. c
11. b
12. b
13. d
14. a
15. a
16. c
17. b
18. c
19. c
20. b
21. a
22. b

PAPER 5

1. c
2. c
3. b
4. b
5. c
6. a
7. a
8. d
9. d
10. b
11. b
12. b
13. b
14. c
15. b
16. a
17. d
18. c
19. d
20. d
21. a
22. b

PAPER 6

1. c
2. d
3. c
4. e
5. c
6. d
7. d
8. b
9. a
10. d
11. c
12. c
13. a
14. c
15. b
16. c
17. c
18. b
19. b
20. c
21. c
22. a

PAPER 7

1. c
2. c
3. c
4. d
5. c
6. e
7. e
8. b
9. d
10. c
11. c
12. a
13. a
14. d
15. c
16. a
17. c
18. b
19. d
20. b
21. d
22. b

PAPER 8

1. b
2. d
3. b
4. b
5. d
6. a
7. c
8. a
9. d
10. d
11. d
12. b
13. a
14. c
15. d
16. c
17. b
18. a
19. c
20. a
21. d
22. b

BLANK PAGE

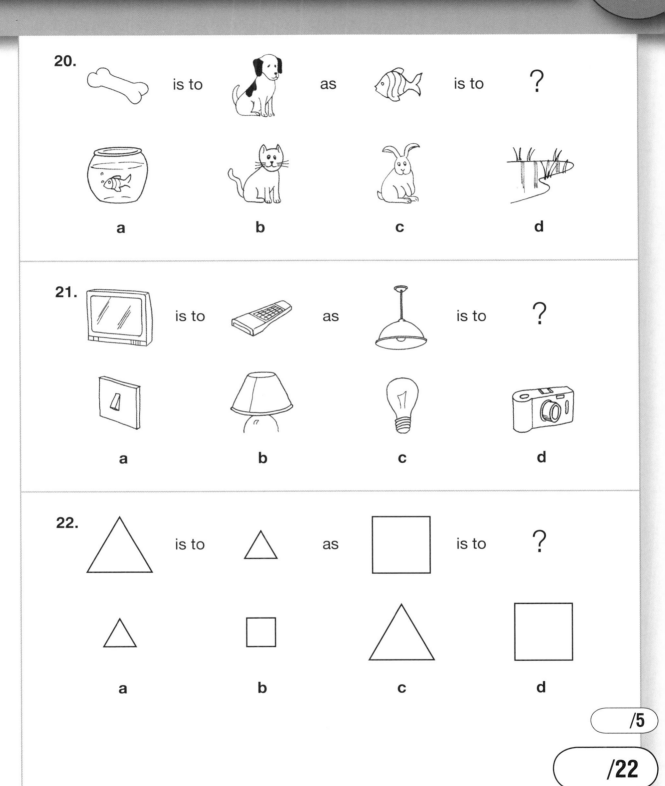

20. is to as is to ?

a b c d

21. is to as is to ?

a b c d

22. is to as is to ?

a b c d

/5

/22

PAPER 5

Example

Which is the odd one out? Circle the letter underneath it.

a   b   c   d

The answer is **d** because the shark is the only animal that lives in the sea.

Now try these. Which is the odd one out? Circle the letter underneath it.

1.

a   b   c   d

2.

a   b   c   d

3.

a   b   c   d

4.

a b c d

5.

  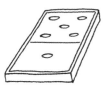 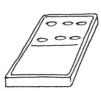

a b c d

6.

a b c d e

7.

a b c d e

/7

Example

Which one comes next? Circle the letter underneath it.

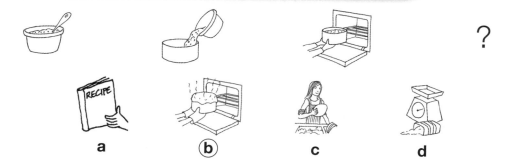

The answer is **b** because it is the next thing that happens in the "story". When you have baked a cake you take it out of the oven.

Now try these. Which one comes next? Circle the letter underneath it.

8.

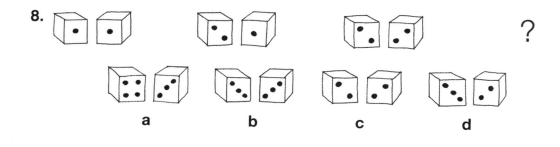

9.

10.

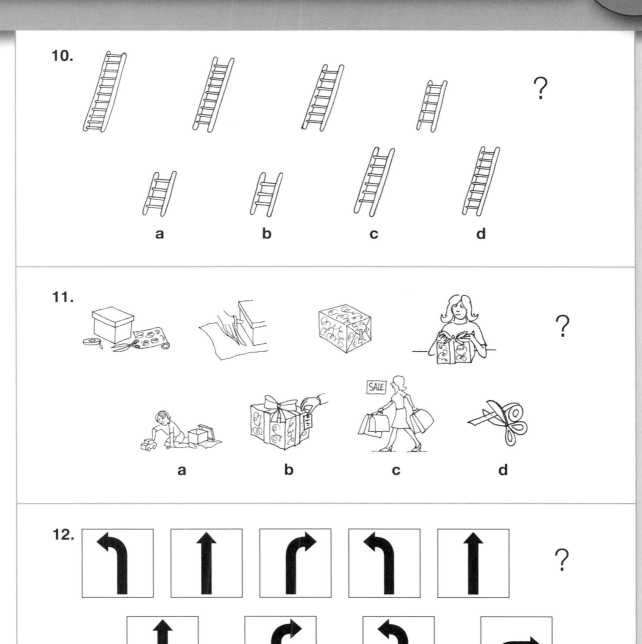

a   b   c   d

11.

a   b   c   d

12.

a   b   c   d

/5

Example

Complete the grid by finding the missing square.
Circle the letter under the square.

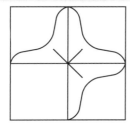

        a   **b**   **c**   **ⓓ**

The answer is **d** because it completes the shape and also finishes the cross in the middle.

Now try these. Circle the letter under the missing square.

13.

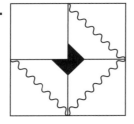

        a   **b**   **c**   **d**

14.

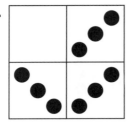

        a   **b**   **c**   **d**

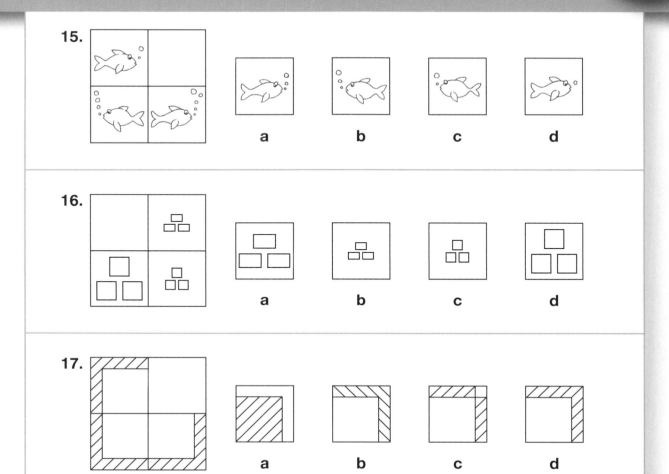

15.

a   b   c   d

16.

a   b   c   d

17.

a   b   c   d

/5

Example

Match the missing part of the second pair in the same way as the first pair. Circle the letter under the missing part.

 is to as is to **?**

a **(b)** **c** **d**

The answer is **b** because you use a toothbrush to brush your teeth and a hairbrush to brush your hair.

Now try these. Circle the letter under the missing part.

18. is to as is to **?**

a **b** **c** **d**

19. is to as is to **?**

a **b** **c** **d**

20.

is to as is to ?

a	**b**	**c**	**d**

21.

is to as is to ?

a	**b**	**c**	**d**

22.

is to as is to ?

a	**b**	**c**	**d**

/5

/22

PAPER 6

Example

Which is the odd one out? Circle the letter underneath it.

| a | b | c | (d) |

The answer is **d** because the shark is the only animal that lives in the sea.

Now try these. Which is the odd one out? Circle the letter underneath it.

1.

| a | b | c | d |

2.

| a | b | c | d |

3.

| a | b | c | d |

4.

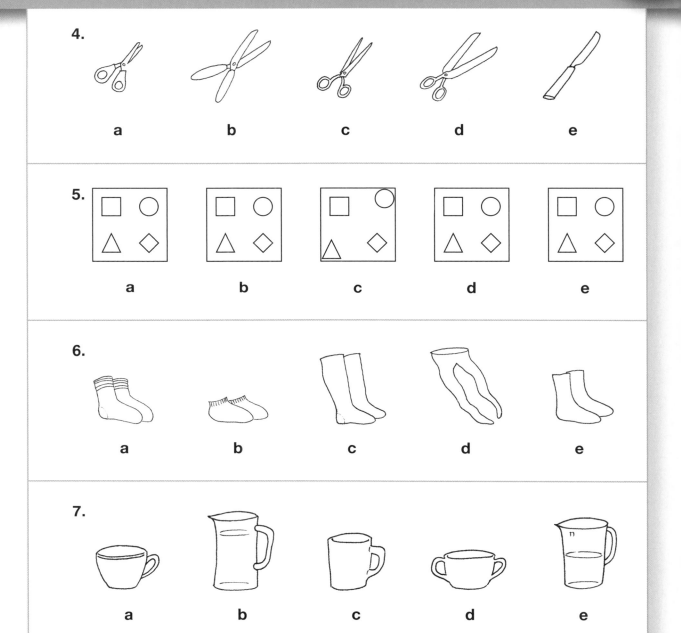

| a | b | c | d | e |

5.

| a | b | c | d | e |

6.

| a | b | c | d | e |

7.

| a | b | c | d | e |

/7

Example

Which one comes next? Circle the letter underneath it.

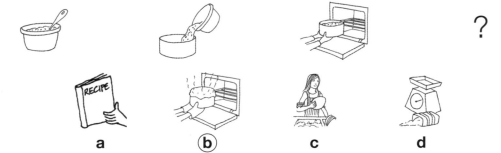

The answer is **b** because it is the next thing that happens in the "story". When you have baked a cake you take it out of the oven.

Now try these. Which one comes next? Circle the letter underneath it.

8.

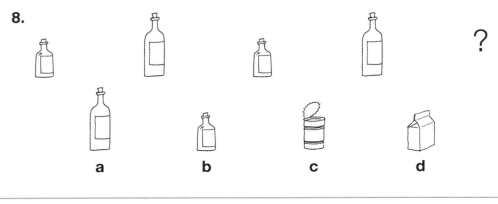

9.

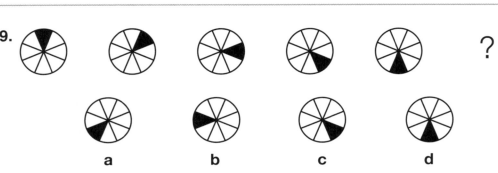

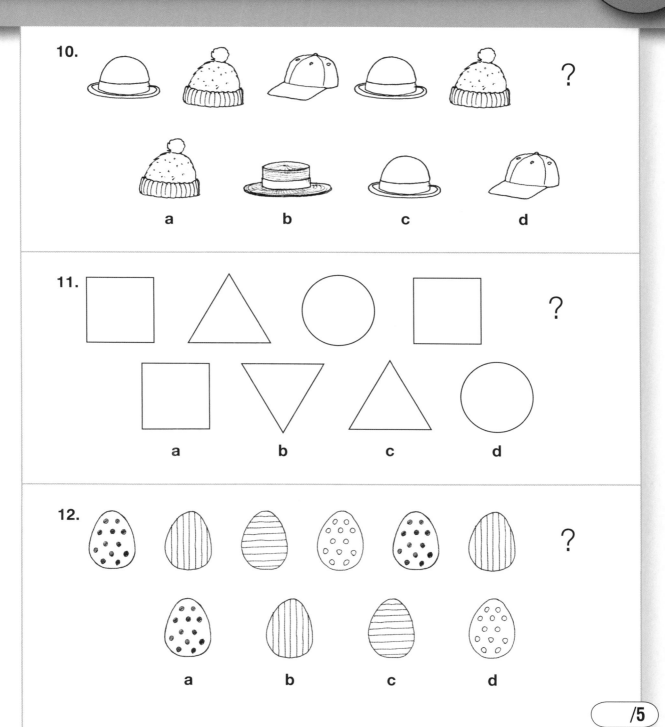

10.

       a   b   c   d

11.

       a   b   c   d

12.

       a   b   c   d

/5

Example

Complete the grid by finding the missing square.
Circle the letter under the square.

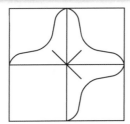

a   b   c   ⓓ

The answer is **d** because it completes the shape and also finishes the cross in the middle.

Now try these. Circle the letter under the missing square.

13.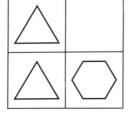

a   b   c   d

14.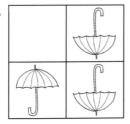

a   b   c   d

15.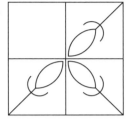

a   b   c   d

16.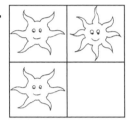

a   b   c   d

17.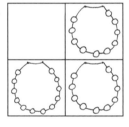

a   b   c   d

/5

Example

Match the missing part of the second pair in the same way as the first pair. Circle the letter under the missing part.

 is to as is to ?

a

(b)

c

d

The answer is **b** because you use a toothbrush to brush your teeth and a hairbrush to brush your hair.

Now try these. Circle the letter under the missing part.

18.

 is to as is to ?

a

b

c

○
d

19.

 is to as is to ?

a

b

c

d

20.

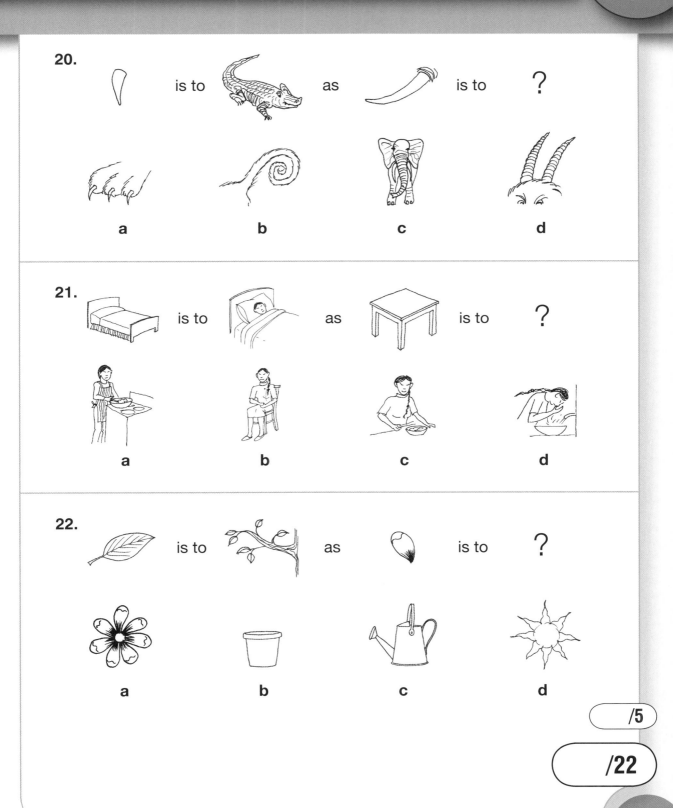

is to ... as ... is to ?

a   b   c   d

21.

is to ... as ... is to ?

a   b   c   d

22.

is to ... as ... is to ?

a   b   c   d

/5

/22

PAPER 7

Example

Which is the odd one out? Circle the letter underneath it.

a   b   c   (d)

The answer is **d** because the shark is the only animal that lives in the sea.

Now try these. Which is the odd one out? Circle the letter underneath it.

1.

a   b   c   d

2.

a   b   c   d

3.

a   b   c   d

4.

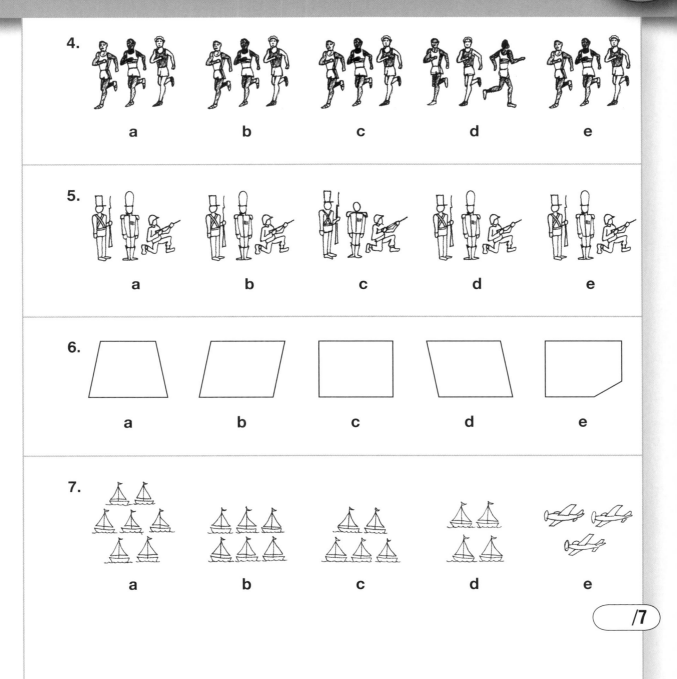

     a   b   c   d   e

5.

     a   b   c   d   e

6.

     a   b   c   d   e

7.

     a   b   c   d   e

/7

Example

Which one comes next? Circle the letter underneath it.

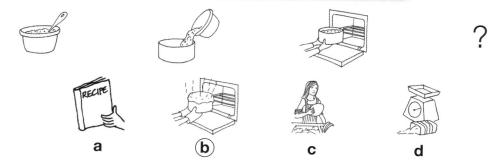

The answer is **b** because it is the next thing that happens in the "story".
When you have baked a cake you take it out of the oven.

Now try these. Which one comes next? Circle the letter underneath it.

8.

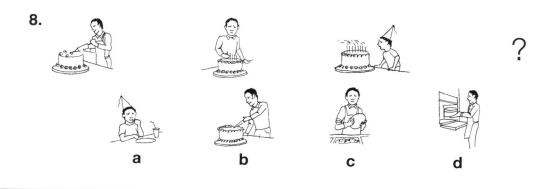

9.

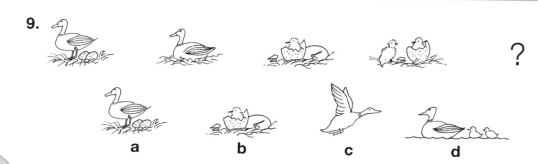

10.

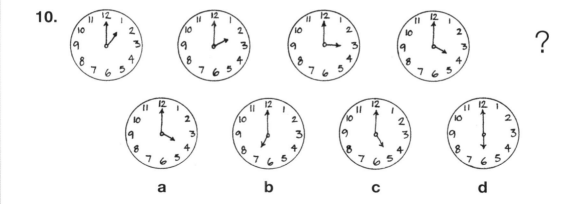

a   b   c   d

11.

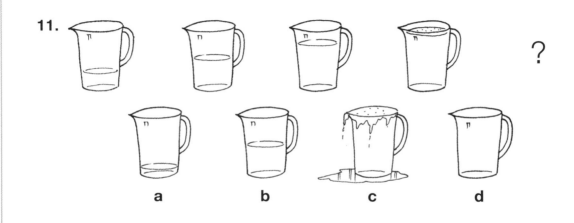

a   b   c   d

12.

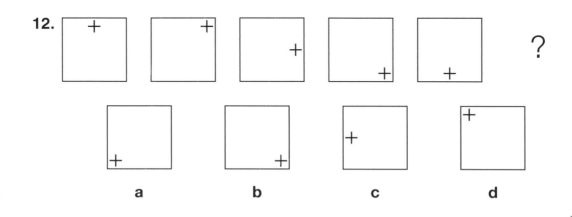

a   b   c   d

/5

Example

Complete the grid by finding the missing square.
Circle the letter under the square.

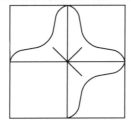

a

b

c

ⓓ

The answer is **d** because it completes the shape and also finishes the cross in the middle.

Now try these. Circle the letter under the missing square.

13.

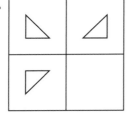

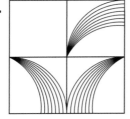

a

b

c

d

14.

a   **b**   **c**   **d**

15.

a   b   c   d

16.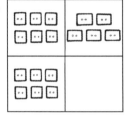

a   b   c   d

17.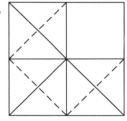

a   b   c   d

/5

Example

Match the missing part of the second pair in the same way as the first pair. Circle the letter under the missing part.

 is to as is to **?**

a

(b)

c

d

The answer is **b** because you use a toothbrush to brush your teeth and a hairbrush to brush your hair.

Now try these. Circle the letter under the missing part.

18.

 is to as is to **?**

a

b

c

d

19.

 is to as is to **?**

a

b

c

d

20.

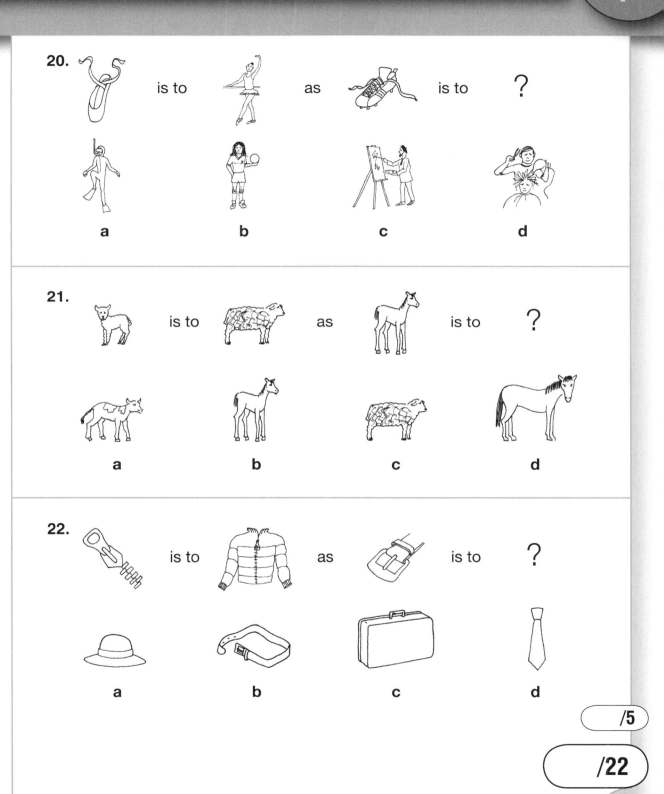

PAPER 8

Example

Which is the odd one out? Circle the letter underneath it.

a

b

c

d

The answer is **d** because the shark is the only animal that lives in the sea.

Now try these. Which is the odd one out? Circle the letter underneath it.

1.

a

b

c

d

2.

a

b

c

d

3.

a

b

c

d

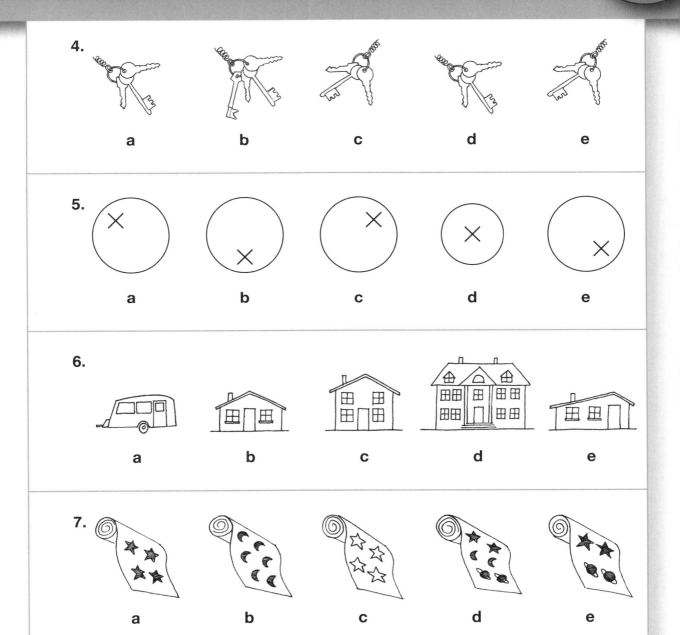

4.

a   b   c   d   e

5.

a   b   c   d   e

6.

a   b   c   d   e

7.

a   b   c   d   e

/7

Example

Which one comes next? Circle the letter underneath it.

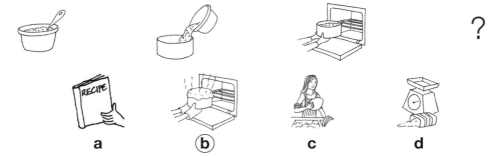

a   (b)   c   d

The answer is **b** because it is the next thing that happens in the "story". When you have baked a cake you take it out of the oven.

Now try these. Which one comes next? Circle the letter underneath it.

8.

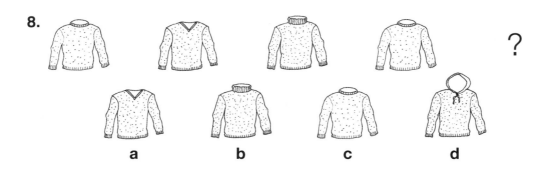

a   b   c   d

9.

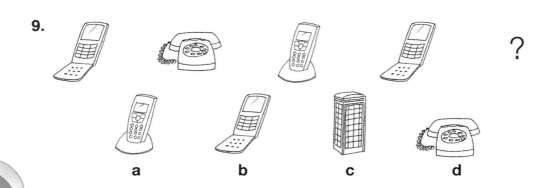

a   b   c   d

10.

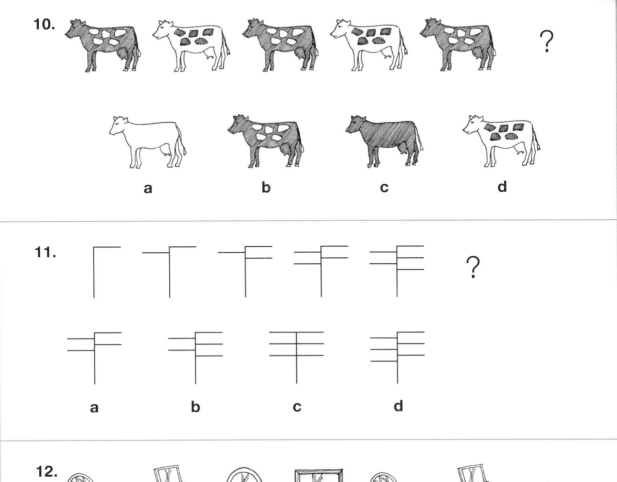

        a   b   c   d

11.

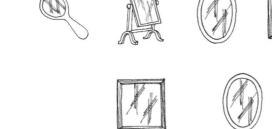

    a   b   c   d

12.

    a   b   c   d

/5

Example

> Complete the grid by finding the missing square.
> Circle the letter under the square.

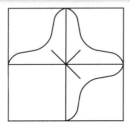

                a   **b**   **c**   **d**

The answer is **d** because it completes the shape and also finishes the cross in the middle.

> Now try these. Circle the letter under the missing square.

13.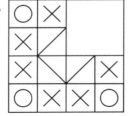

     a   **b**   **c**   **d**

14.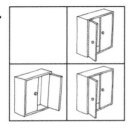

     a   **b**   **c**   **d**

15.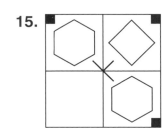

a   b   c   d

16.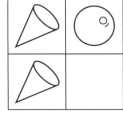

a   b   c   d

17.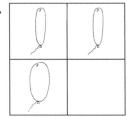

a   b   c   d

/5

Example

Match the missing part of the second pair in the same way as the first pair. Circle the letter under the missing part.

 is to as is to

a

(b)

c

d

The answer is **b** because you use a toothbrush to brush your teeth and a hairbrush to brush your hair.

Now try these. Circle the letter under the missing part.

18.

 is to as is to

a

b

c

d

19.

 is to as is to

a

b

c

d

20.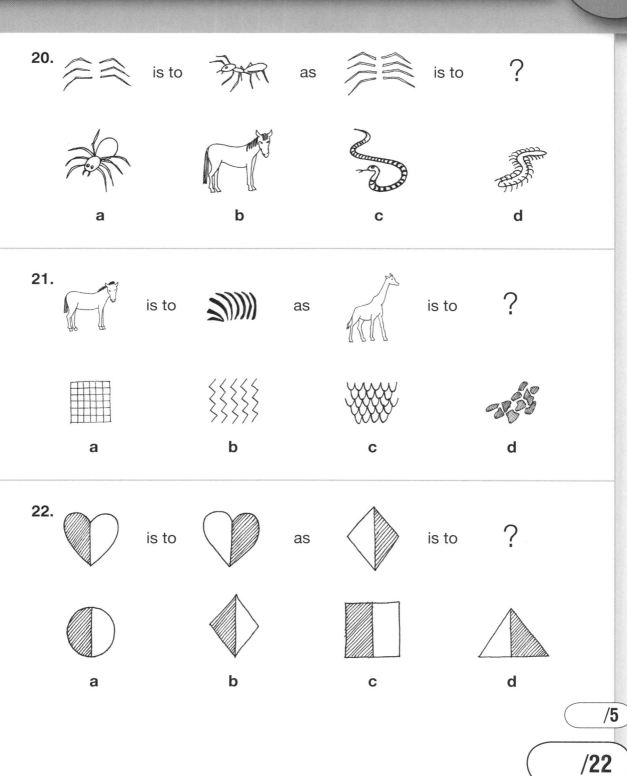

21.

22.

Progress grid

Total marks ▼

Paper ▼

22

20

15

10

5

0

Date ▶

Now colour in your score!